MW01038637

3D FACIAL APPROXIMATION LAB MANUAL

Susan Hayes PhD MFA

www.researchgate.net/profile/Susan_Hayes

ISBN: 978-0-9872066-3-3 (paperback)
ISBN: 978-0-9872066-2-6 (ebook)

Front cover: 3D facial approximation of A20. Back cover: 2D facial approximation of A20 lateral outlines. Unless otherwise specified all images in this publication are the work of Susan Hayes.

CONTENTS

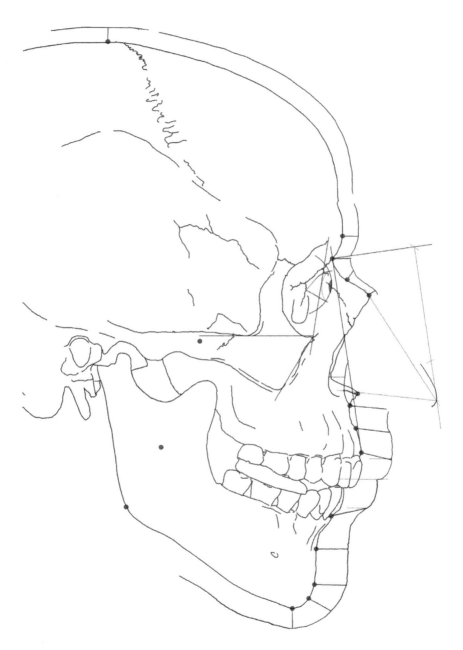

Figure 1. Lab Manual 3D Facial Approximation
Estimation of the facial features, lateral view.

OVERVIEW

This introductory 3D Lab Manual is designed so that anyone, no matter what their interests and background, can gain hands-on experience in estimating facial appearance from the skull.

What's covered here has grown from a science course I developed in 2006 for delivery in Universities, Colleges, Artist Societies, Museums and Schools, and which has proven to be equally popular in Australia, New Zealand, the United Kingdom, Indonesia, Thailand and The Philippines. In 2011, I published a 3D Lab Manual (Hayes, 2012) to accompany this course. This is a much needed revision, update and reformat of the Lab Manual, but the focus remains the same: to provide a clear, step-by-step guide so that non-specialists can independently experience this fascinating and highly multidisciplinary field of applied research.

A Lab Manual is essentially a work-book, and this one presents most of the information in pictures. There is minimal text support, and what text is provided is academic-*lite*. The core information is:

   (i)   the materials needed to get started
   (ii)   some basic information about the human skull and teeth
   (iii)   a structured guide to sculpting the underlying anatomy
   (iv)   a structured guide to sculpting surface appearance
   (v)   references and acknowledgements.

If you genuinely want to know more about the field of facial approximation, seek out articles that adhere to standard scientific conventions, have been internationally peer reviewed, and are published in reputable academic journals. This 3D Lab Manual, as with many forensic handbooks, is none of these things. The *References* section includes some of the more relevant research for estimating the face from the skull. But keep in mind that a few of the methods are from the techniques used in *forensic facial reconstruction* — Karen T. Taylor (2001) is highly recommended — and some of these methods have still not (yet) been scientifically verified. Also, most research publications, including my own, apply methods that are revised when more robust findings become available.

For this 3D Lab Manual, the main thing is that you have the experience. Certainly you will never look at a living human face in quite the same way again.

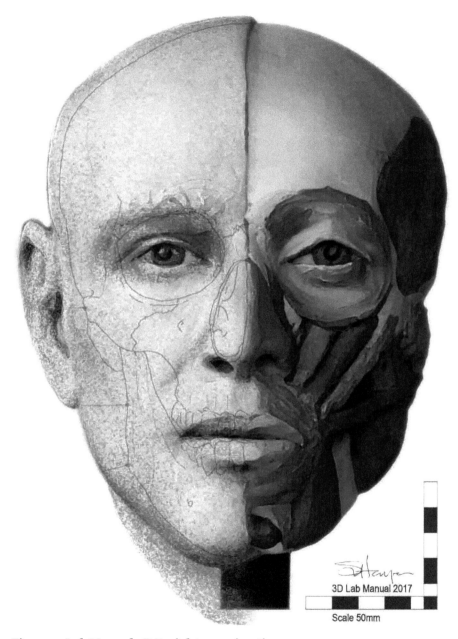

3D Lab Manual 2017

Scale 50mm

Figure 2. Lab Manual 3D Facial Approximation
Frontal view of a split clay model, partially overlaid with the computer graphic estimation of facial appearance.

Facial Approximation

Facial approximation is similar to the extraordinarily popular method most often referred to as *forensic facial reconstruction*. Facial approximation is not, however, a widely used approach. If you really want to know, I've written a number of papers specifically highlighting the similarities and differences between the different methods for palaeoanthropological, archaeological and forensic applications (e.g. Hayes *et al.* 2017, Hayes 2016, Hayes 2014, Hayes *et al.* 2013).

Ethics of the Dead

Although a replica skull is used here (and you can adapt the instructions to a different anatomical model), the patterns of the bones were taken from the remains of a once living individual. Some of the quirks in the shapes may be due to the casting and duplication process, but not all. Most of the details are because replicas are cast directly from the remains of a real person who lived all that a unique human life entails.

I do not know when this particular person died or how they lived. All I can say with any certainty is that this replica is 3B Scientific's *Classic Human Skull Model*, and the product code is A20. When I work with human remains I refer to them by their collection or case number, and so I refer to this individual as A20. This is not to depersonalise A20, but to respect that they already have a name. However, as with most of my archaeological research, I don't know their name, and probably never will.

The absence of third molars might indicate that A20 was a young adult when they died (Cunha *et al.* 2009), and their youth may also be why they became a replica skull. Unfortunately, no-one from the manufacturer has ever replied to my requests for information regarding population affinity and sex. In the early days I ran labs where A20 was assumed to be a European female, and others where A20 was taken to be male and/or of indeterminate sex (see the images of student work at the end of *Part A Underlying Anatomy*).

For this Lab Manual A20 is assumed to be male because the replica skeleton to which A20 is often attached has been called 'Stan' by the manufacturer (skulls are not very reliable for estimating sex). Also, A20 has been on sale since a period when European male was synonymous with 'Classic Human'.

An assumption of European maleness is also useful (pedagogically) because most students lack the necessary skills and experience of a professional sculptor. Non-artists tend to think working in clay is easier than drawing, but the reality is the reverse. It takes years of concentrated effort to be able to control the medium and sculpt what you intend. This is possibly why students (and most non-artists) tend to produce results that are 'chunky', which is more in keeping with robust, more masculine facial features.

Finally, and most importantly, I strongly suspect that an afterlife as a replica skull was not something A20 ever anticipated or volunteered for. Therefore, as with all human remains, it is fitting that we respect and acknowledge the debt we owe to A20, and all of the people whose remains have formed the basis of a replica skull. These individuals are all unique, and in their uniqueness they help us to further our understanding and appreciation of every human face, both living and deceased.

Figure 3. Workshop in the Chapel, East Perth Cemeteries (Western Australia 2012).
Photographer Gina Pickering, National Trust.
Reproduced with kind permission.

GETTING STARTED

Materials

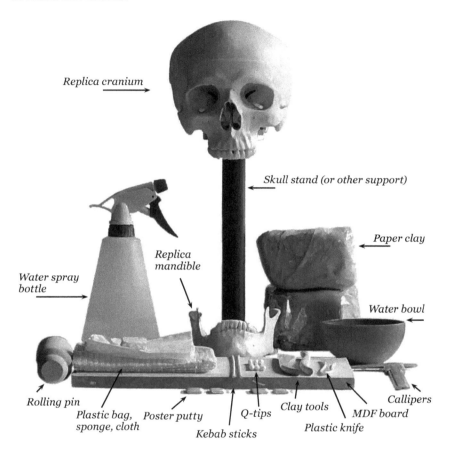

Replica cranium

Skull stand (or other support)

Paper clay

Replica mandible

Water spray bottle

Water bowl

Rolling pin

Plastic bag, sponge, cloth

Poster putty

Q-tips

Kebab sticks

Clay tools

Plastic knife

MDF board

Callipers

Figure 4. Materials.
This is the equipment I currently use for teaching, but only a replica skull, clay and some kind of support are essential, and poster putty if the mandible is unattached.

Whenever possible I prefer to teach using terracotta (brown) and earthenware (grey) paper clay. Using two colours helps differentiate the anatomical features, and paper clay is both kind to novices and capable of producing very fine results. During a course for gifted school children, a student took advantage of the fibres that are threaded through paper clay and modelled individual eyelashes. Sculpting, however, can be accomplished using any regular modelling clay of any colour(s), though a fine grog is probably easier to work with.

Articulating the Mandible

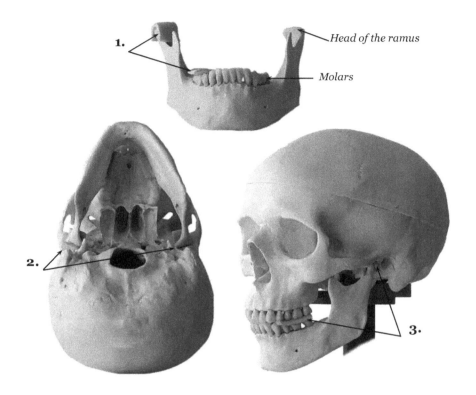

1.

Head of the ramus

Molars

2.

3.

Figure 5. Articulating the Mandible.
Most replica skulls have the mandible attached, but this results in clenched teeth.

This method for articulating the jaw is based on recommendations from the very gifted North American forensic artist, Karen T. Taylor (2001). In addition to securing the jaw to the cranium, the putty also simulates an auricular disc at the tempero-mandibular joint (TMJ) and a very approximate variant of the 'freeway space' (Johnson *et al.* 2002) that occurs between the molars.

1. Place poster putty (or similar) over the head of the ramus and along the back molars (on both sides of the mandible);
2. Place the putty covered head of the ramus inside the hollow which forms the capsule for the TMJ;
3. Make sure the mandible is securely attached at both the TMJ and freeway space to avoid a sudden jaw-drop.

Parts of the Skull

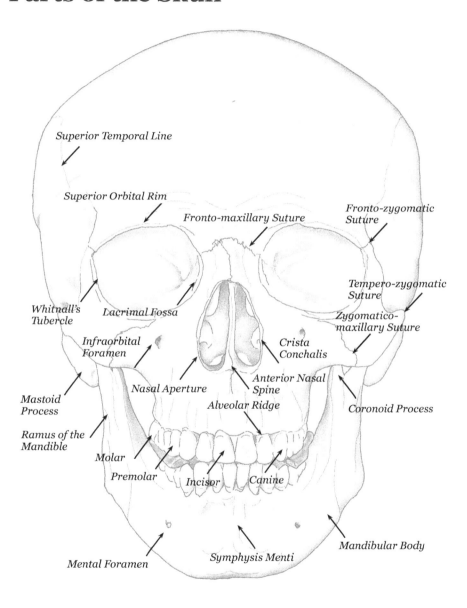

Superior Temporal Line

Superior Orbital Rim

Fronto-maxillary Suture

Fronto-zygomatic Suture

Tempero-zygomatic Suture

Whitnall's Tubercle

Lacrimal Fossa

Zygomatico-maxillary Suture

Infraorbital Foramen

Crista Conchalis

Anterior Nasal Spine

Nasal Aperture

Mastoid Process

Alveolar Ridge

Coronoid Process

Ramus of the Mandible

Molar

Premolar

Incisor

Canine

Mental Foramen

Symphysis Menti

Mandibular Body

Figure 6. Parts of the Skull and Teeth: Frontal View.
A human skull is comprised of the teeth, the cranium (which includes the neurocranium and facial bones) and the mandible (jaw bone). This illustration, together with Figure 7 (over the page) includes the major areas of the skull that are of interest in estimating the face. There is a lot more to the skull and teeth than is covered here.

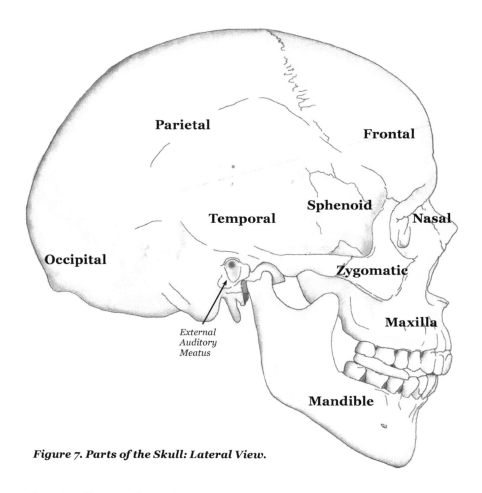

Parietal

Frontal

Sphenoid

Nasal

Temporal

Occipital

Zygomatic

External Auditory Meatus

Maxilla

Mandible

Figure 7. Parts of the Skull: Lateral View.

facial Soft Tissue Depths

A human skull covered in depth markers is probably the most iconic image of a *forensic facial reconstruction*. For this 3D Lab Manual the facial Soft Tissue Depths (fSTDs) have only been applied to the computer graphic illustrations, not the clay work. This is because as an introductory, largely experiential workbook, accurately applying fSTD markers and angles slows down the work (the fSTDs require careful sculpting around them), and it's possible to become focussed on the depth points to the expense of learning about the underlying anatomy.

Estimating the face from the skull requires experience and knowledge across a range of fields and sub-fields, so I recommend using the tissue depths as a general guide, at least in the first instance.

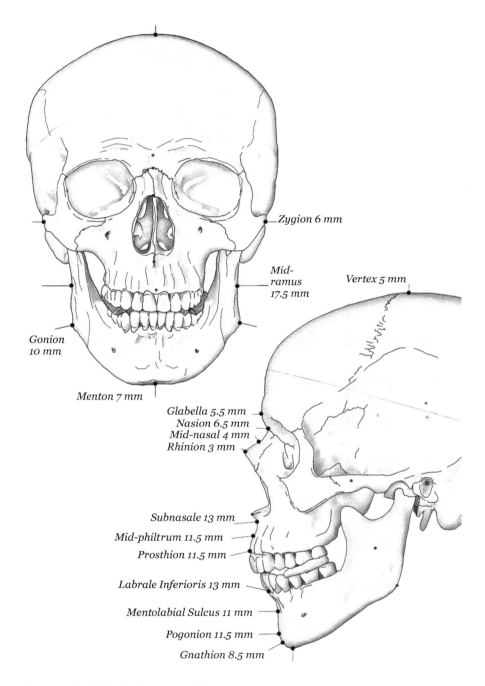

Figure 8. facial Soft Tissue Depths.
Different researchers have different names for the craniofacial landmarks, so it is always a good idea to define and illustrate them. This subset of facial Soft Tissue Depths (fSTD)are adapted from a robust set of weighted global averages (Stephan and Simpson 2008); see also Aulsebrook et al. 1996.

About the Instructional Pages

The instructional pages cover modelling the face from the skull, working from the underlying anatomical features (Part A), to modelling the surface appearance (Part B) as a split model, where only half the face is covered by 'skin'. In both Part A and Part B the instructions for each aspect cover two pages (see Figure 9 below).

The anatomical features applied in this facial approximation are stylised representations, similar to how they appear in anatomy books. The translations of the Latin and Greek anatomical names are from Lisowski and Oxnard 2007, and the anatomical descriptions reference information in Standring 2008, McMinn *et al.* 1999, Duchenne de Boulogne 1990 and Warwick and Williams 1973. The facial Soft Tissue Depths are only included in the comparatively more accurate computer graphic estimations.

Separate instructional pages cover the modelling of the facial features (e.g. mouth, nose and eyes). Although the computer graphic estimations include verified facial approximation methods, the clay modelling illustrations show techniques that may help non-artists model a facial feature that looks similar to what they intend.

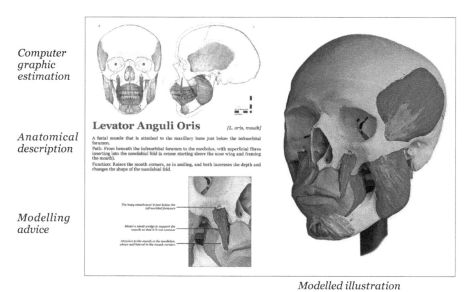

Computer graphic estimation

Anatomical description

Modelling advice

Modelled illustration

Figure 9. Instructional Page Example.

PART A:
UNDERLYING ANATOMY

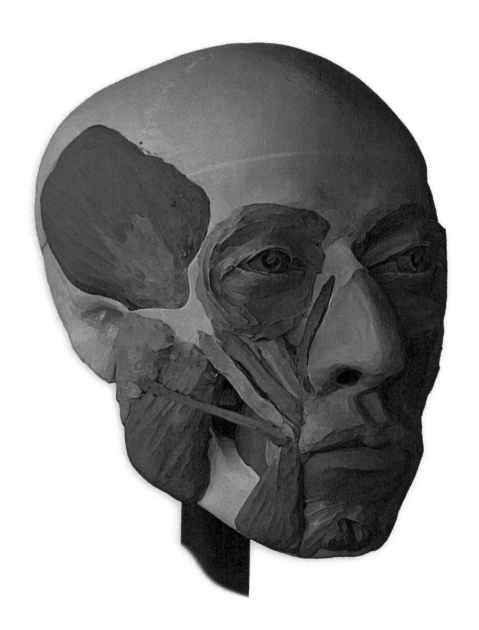

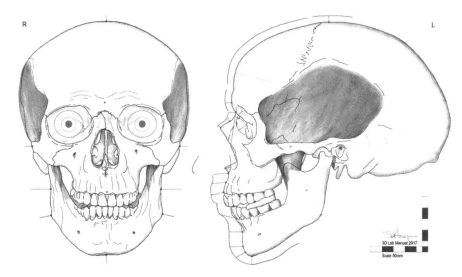

Temporalis

[L. tempora, the temples; tempus, time]

A fan-shaped muscle that fills out the side of the head. The fibres converge as a tendon and pass through the zygomatic arch.

Path: From the inferior temporal line to the coronoid process.

Function: Raises the mandible to close the mouth and contributes to the sideways grinding movement of the jaw. The temporalis can be felt when used to clench the teeth.

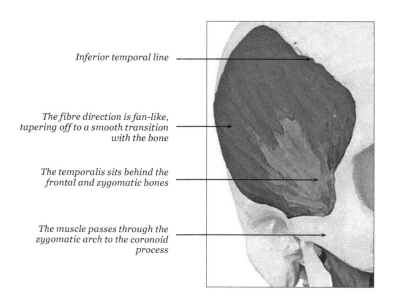

Inferior temporal line

The fibre direction is fan-like, tapering off to a smooth transition with the bone

The temporalis sits behind the frontal and zygomatic bones

The muscle passes through the zygomatic arch to the coronoid process

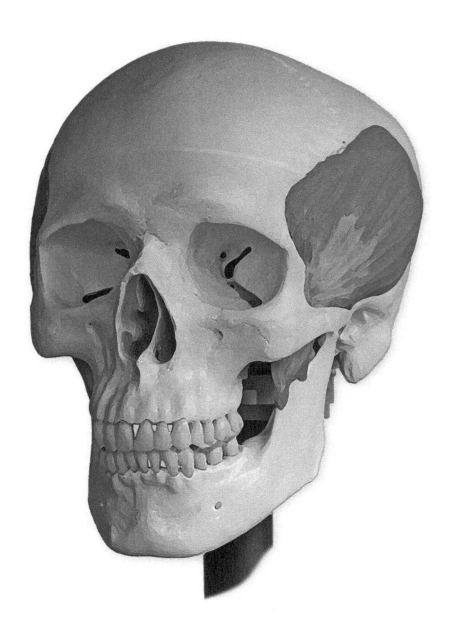

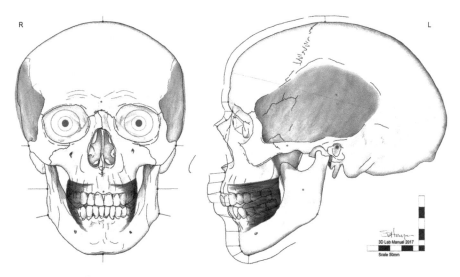

Buccinator

[L. bucca, cheek]

A thin, quadrilateral muscle located on the inside of the cheek. Sometimes called the 'trumpeter muscle'.

Path: From above the upper molars and below the lower molars to converge with the muscles of the mouth.

Function: Compresses the cheeks when full of air as in blowing, and during chewing to keep food passing between the molars.

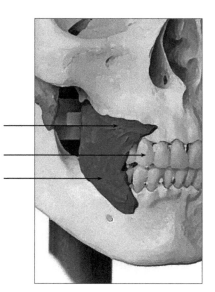

The upper and lower fibres continue and merge with the muscles of the mouth

The canines are left exposed for modelling the mouth

The central fibres criss-cross and converge near the mouth corners

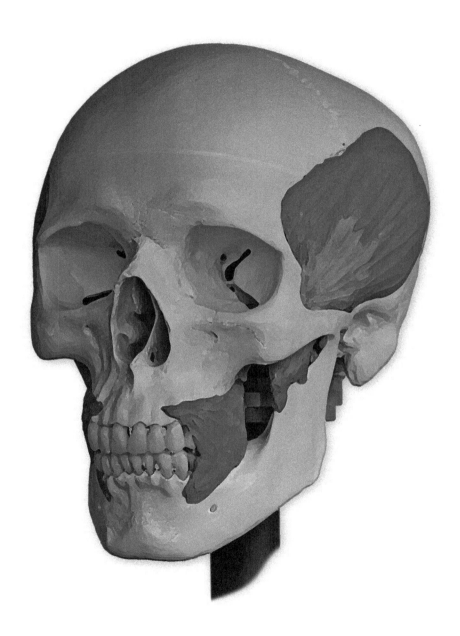

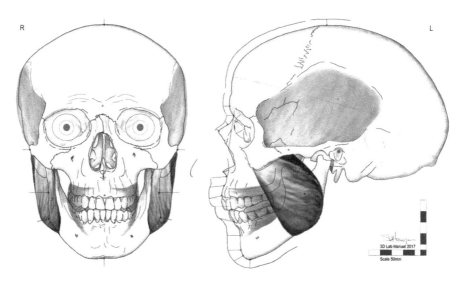

Masseter

[G. masseter, chewer]

A comparatively thick, quadrilateral muscle composed of three layers (superficial, middle, deep), but only the superficial layer is approximated here.

Path: From the lower border of the zygomatic bone to the body and angle of the ramus.

Function: Brings the back teeth together for grinding during chewing. Can be seen along the cheek when the teeth are clenched.

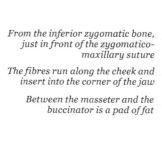

From the inferior zygomatic bone, just in front of the zygomatico-maxillary suture

The fibres run along the cheek and insert into the corner of the jaw

Between the masseter and the buccinator is a pad of fat

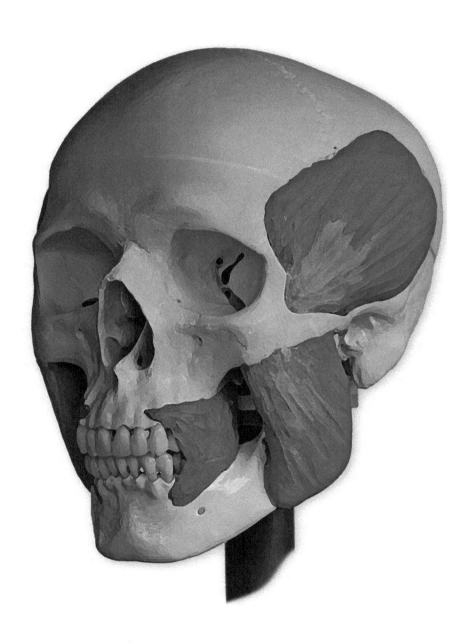

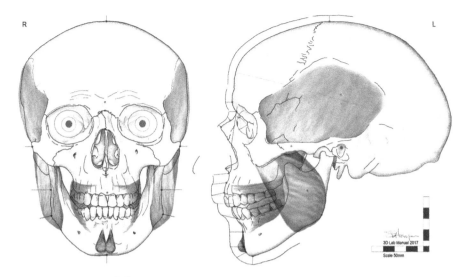

Mentalis

[L. mentum, chin]

A conical bundle of muscle fibres located either side of the symphysis menti, which is a ridge running vertically down the centre of the mental (chin) part of the mandible.

Path: The fibres attach either side of the symphysis menti, then run downwards, inwards, and outwards through the fat of the chin to attach to the skin.

Function: Raises and thrusts out the lower lip. Activation causes a dimpling effect, which is associated with expressions of doubt or disdain. Sometimes called the 'pouting muscle'.

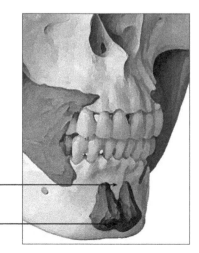

The bony attachments are either side of the symphysis menti

Conical bundles meeting at the base where the fibres extend through the fat

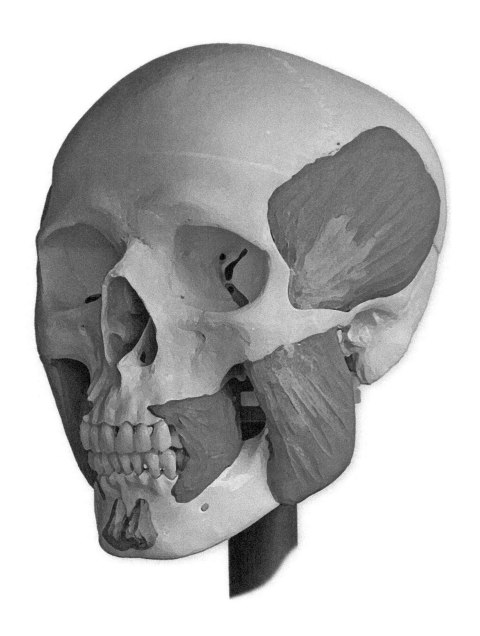

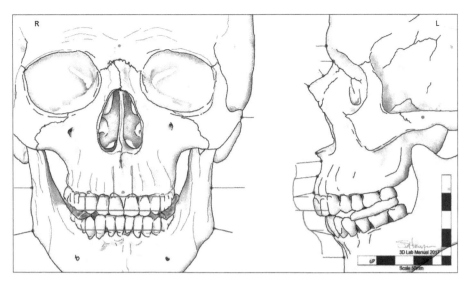

MOUTH

The mouth corners are in the region of the canine-premolar junction, and in a frontal view roughly correspond with the medial edge of the iris and the location of the mental foramen. The height of the lips may be related to the height of the central incisors. The oral fissure may be about two-thirds down the height of the central incisors, and philtrum width may be similar to the width between the centres of the central incisors. See the references below for more information about each of these relationships.

Here, the mouth has been sculpted in two parts: lower lip followed by upper lip. But as can be seen on the following pages, the mouth muscle is circular in shape, with the muscle fibres all interconnecting.

References: Stephan 2003,
Wilkinson et al. 2003, Song
et al. 2002, Taylor 2001,
Gerasimov 1955.

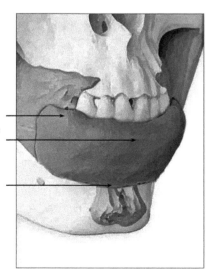

The mouth corners are outwards from the canine-premolar junction

The lower lip covers about one-third of the height of the central incisors

The lower fibres converge with the mentalis

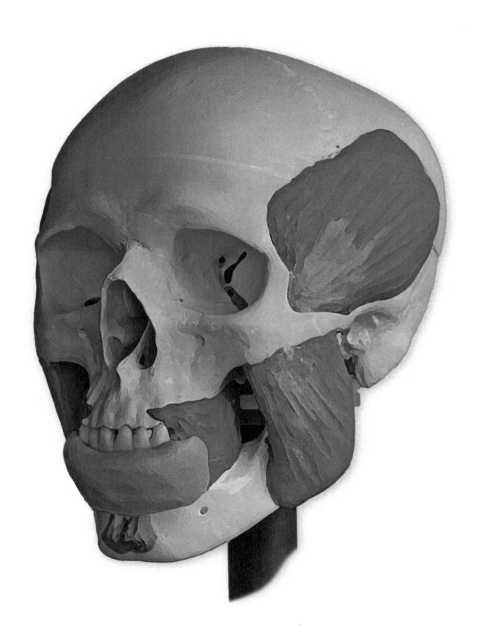

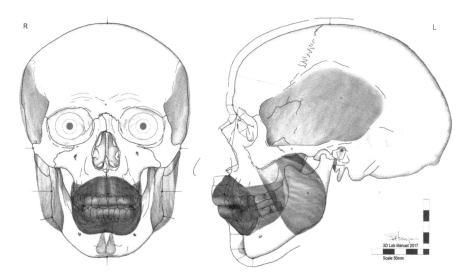

Orbicularis Oris

[L. orbis, circular; oris, mouth]

Four relatively independent quadrants, with each quadrant containing two fan-shaped segments. The stems of the fans are located at the modiolus, which is a 'hub' of muscles located outside and up from the mouth corner.

Path: The quadrants flow in a roughly circular direction, with no attachments to the bone.

Function: Brings the lips together and thrusts them outwards, as in kissing.

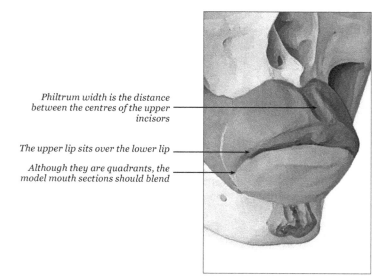

Philtrum width is the distance between the centres of the upper incisors

The upper lip sits over the lower lip

Although they are quadrants, the model mouth sections should blend

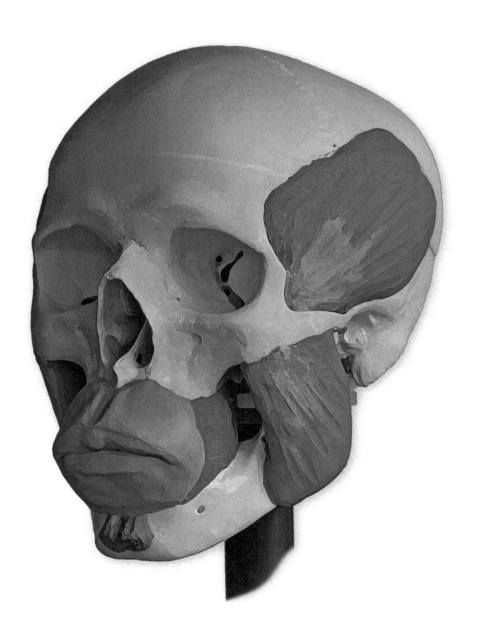

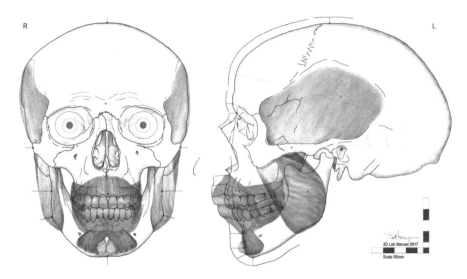

Depressor Labii Inferioris

[L. labium, lip]

A quadrilateral muscle located between the symphysis menti and the mental foramen. The superficial fibres contain fatty tissue.

Path: From the lower jaw, upwards and inwards to intermingle with the mouth muscles.

Function: Pulls the lower lip downwards and outwards; activation occurs during both mastication and in the facial expression of irony.

The upper fibres continue and blend with the mouth

Medial to the mental foramen and converges at the symphysis menti

The lower fibres blend with the platysma, which is not modelled

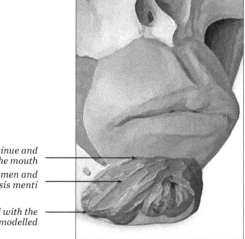

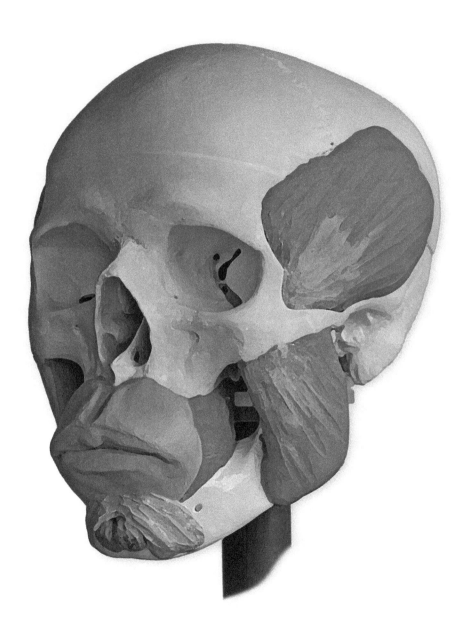

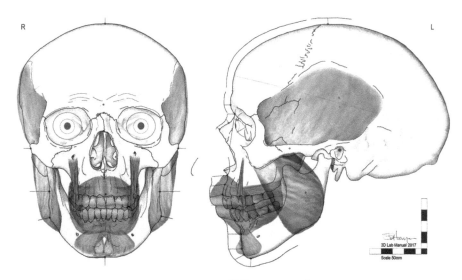

Levator Anguli Oris

[L. oris, mouth]

A facial muscle that is attached to the maxillary bone just below the infraorbital foramen.

Path: From beneath the infraorbital foramen to the modiolus (mouth hub), with superficial fibres inserting into the nasolabial fold (a crease starting above the nose wing and framing the mouth).

Function: Raises the mouth corners, as in smiling; both increases the depth and changes the shape of the nasolabial fold.

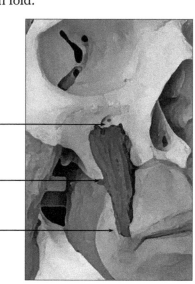

The bony attachment is just below the infraorbital foramen

Model a small wedge to support the muscle so that it is not concave

Attaches to the mouth at the modiolus, a hub located above and lateral to the mouth corners

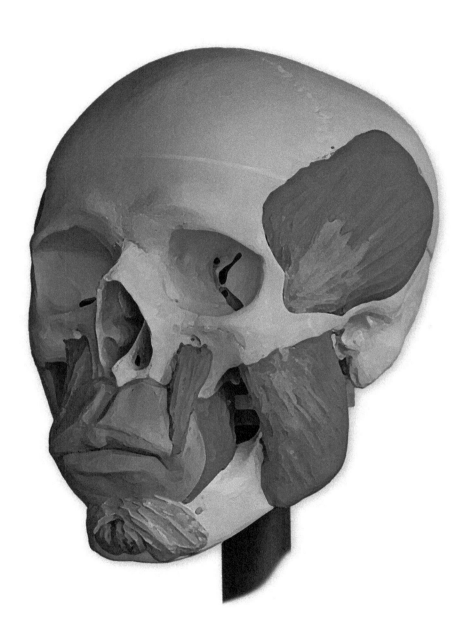

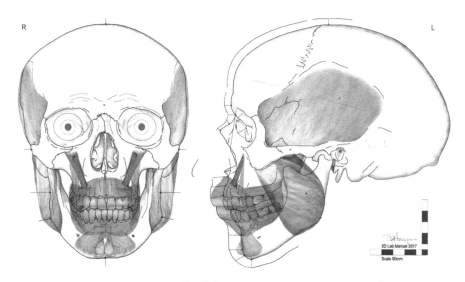

Levator Labii Superioris

[L. labium, lip]

A thin, gently fanning muscle that starts above, and crosses over, much of the underlying levator anguli oris.

Path: Above the infraorbital foramen and below the inferior rim of the orbit running down to insert into, and blend with, the upper quadrants of the mouth muscle.

Function: A muscle associated with crying, it deepens the nasiolabial furrow during expressions of sadness and/or seriousness.

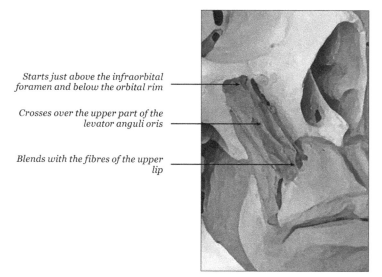

Starts just above the infraorbital foramen and below the orbital rim

Crosses over the upper part of the levator anguli oris

Blends with the fibres of the upper lip

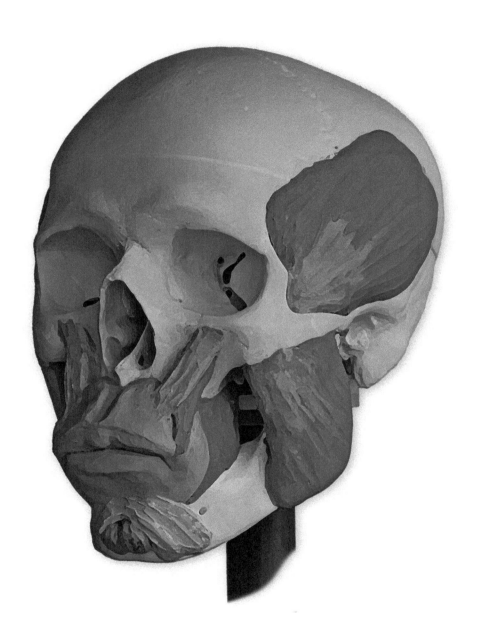

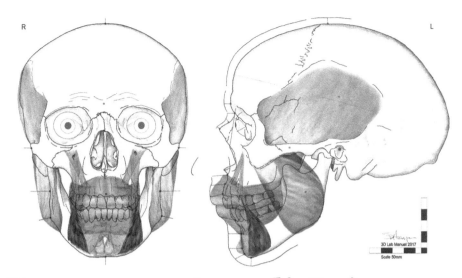

Depressor Anguli Oris

[L. oris, mouth]

A mirror muscle to the levator anguli oris, the depressor anguli oris is roughly triangular in shape, crosses over part of the depressor labii inferioris and attaches at the modiolus.

Path: Attachment to the mandible is slightly to the side, and below, the depressor labii inferioris and the upper fibres blend at the modiolus.

Function: Lowers the mouth corners and shifts them laterally. Associated with expressions of sadness and disgust.

The upper fibres blend with the other muscles at the modiolus (mouth hub)

The lower section crosses over the depressor labii inferioris

As with the depressor labii inferioris, the lower fibres merge with the platysma

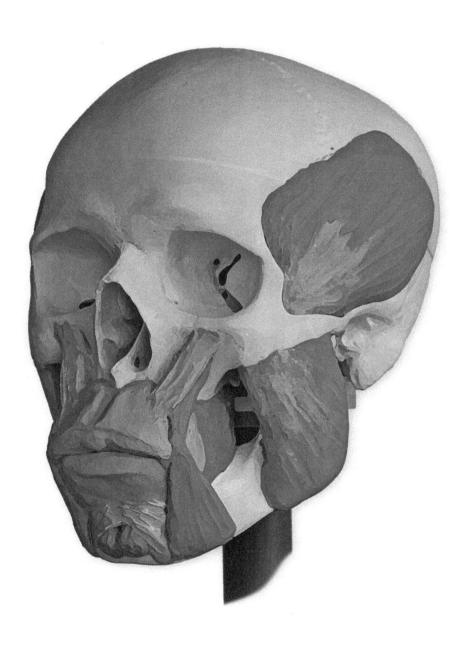

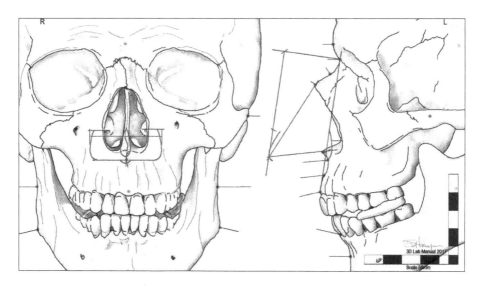

NOSE

Nasal shape is largely determined by the cartilages, and nose projection can be estimated using an algorithm that includes the dimensions of the nasal aperture. Maximum nasal aperture width is roughly three fifths the maximum width of the nasal wings, and the height of the nasal wings can be estimated from the crista conchalis. The angle of the nasal shaft is indicated by the anterior nasal bones, the location of the nasal tip may be related to the angle of the nasal aperture floor, and nasal tip shape may correspond to the shape of the anterior nasal spine. See the references below for more information about each of these relationships.

References: Mala 2013, Ullrich and Stephan 2011, Rynn et al. 2009, Anderson et al. 2008, Gerasimov 1955.

The nasal shaft direction is indicated by the anterior edges of the nasal bones

Border of the nasal aperture

The height of the nasal wings corresponds to the crista conchalis

The direction of the nasal tip is related to the angle of the floor of the nasal aperture base

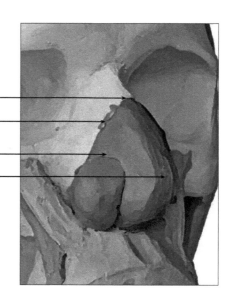

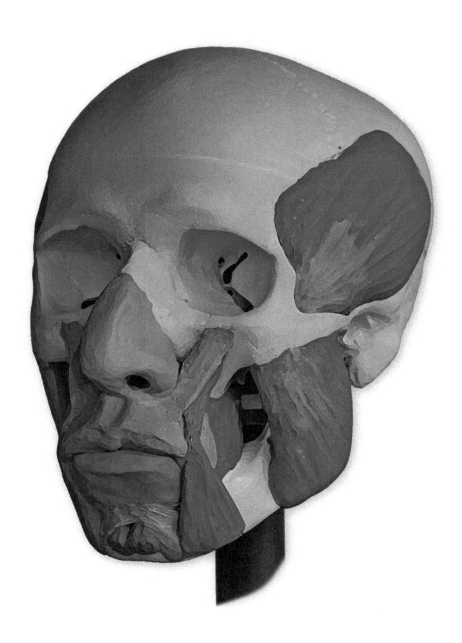

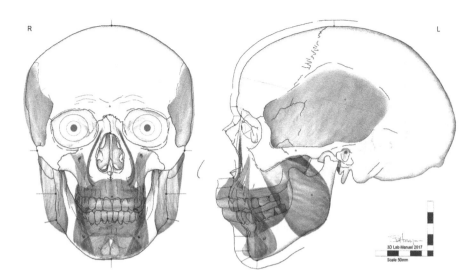

Levator Labii Superioris Alaeque Nasi *[L. ala, wing; nasus, nose]*

This muscle runs along the side of the nose and blends with the levator labii superioris and orbicularis oris.

Path: Below the fronto-maxillary suture to the nasal wing and medial part of the upper lip.

Function: Dilates the nostrils and raises the upper lip. Associated with weeping and expressions of disgust.

A delicate muscle that is attached to the maxilla below the fronto-maxillary suture

The medial part inserts into the nose wings to dilate the nostrils

The lateral part blends with the levator labii superioris and the upper mouth

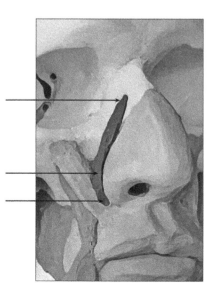

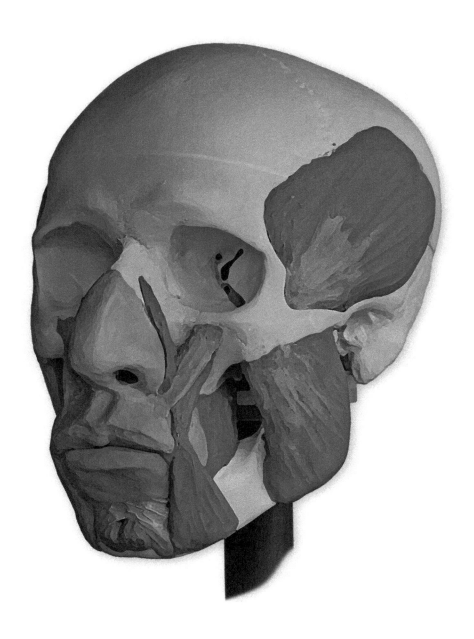

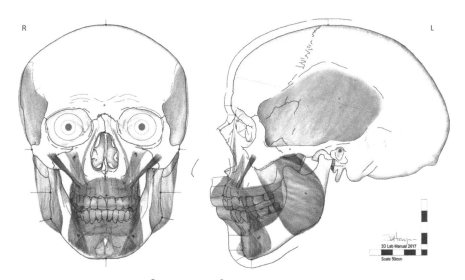

Zygomatic Minor

[G. zygoma, yoke]

One of a pair of strap muscles that help form the shape of the cheeks. The zygomatic muscles can be highly variable on different individuals.

Path: Starting lateral to the zygomatico-maxillary suture, this muscle inserts into the upper lip between the levator labii superioris and the levator anguli oris.

Function: Raises the upper lip so that the teeth are exposed. Working together with other muscles of the upper lip, it produces a lip curl that is associated with smiling, smugness, contempt and/or disdain.

Attachment to the bone is lateral to the zygomatico-maxillary suture

To prevent the model being concave, build a supporting wedge beneath this muscle

Inserts into the upper lip between the two levator muscles

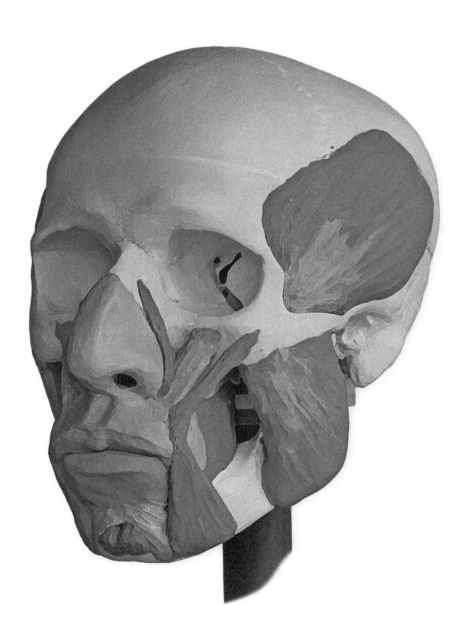

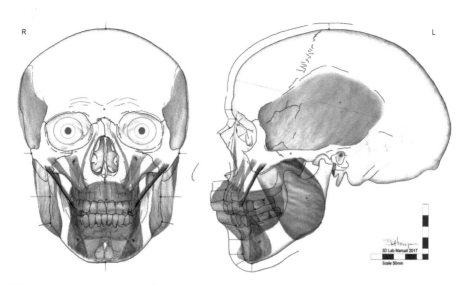

Zygomatic Major

[G. zygoma, yoke]

The longer of the two zygomatic muscles that span the cheeks, this muscle (like the zygomatic minor) can be highly variable.

Path: Starting between the zygomatico-temporal and zygomatico-maxillary sutures, and beneath the start of zygomatic minor, this muscle inserts into the mouth at the modiolus (mouth hub).

Function: Raises the corner of the mouth upwards and outwards, and is associated with expressions of joy, such as smiling and laughter.

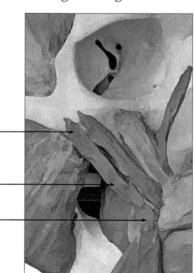

This muscle starts beneath the attachment of the zygomatic minor

As with the zygomatic minor, a wedge of support will be needed

The zygomatic major blends with the other muscles at the modiolus

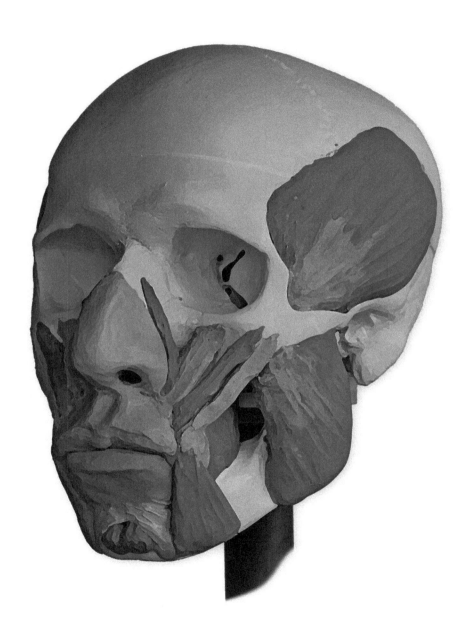

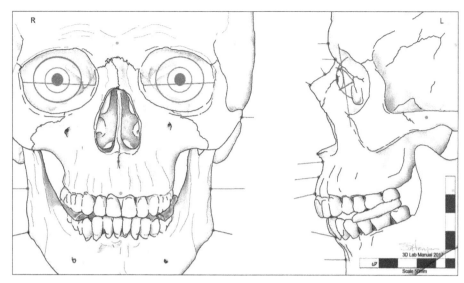

EYES

Here the eyeballs have been sculpted much larger than life. The human eyeball is ~23 mm in diameter, and is located slightly superior, and lateral, to the centre of the bony orbits. The eyeball sits within the extremities of the orbital rims, with the iris extending beyond this by ~3-4 mm. The fissure of the eyelids is estimated from the lacrimal fossa (tear hole) and Whitnall's tubercle (a small bump on the lateral walls of the orbital bones). See the references below for more information about each of these relationships.

References: Stephan et al. 2009, Stephan 2002, Gerasimov 1955, Wolff 1948, Whitnall 1911.

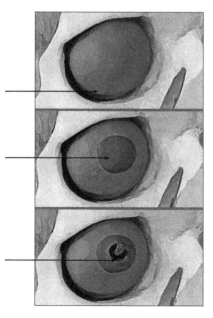

This modelled eyeball is larger than life, but still sits within both orbital rims

The iris bulges out from the eyeball, and is approximately 10-12 mm in diameter

The 'horseshoe' shape of the pupil suggests the direction of the light

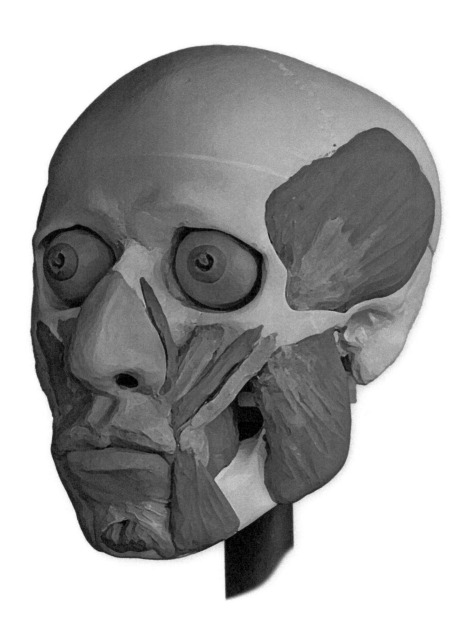

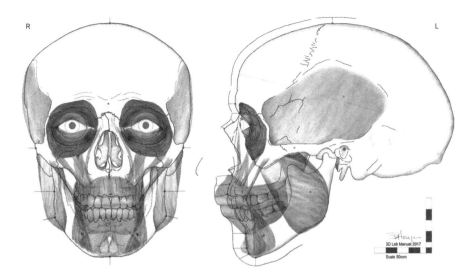

Orbicularis Oculi

[L. orbis, circular; oculus, eye]

A sphincter muscle that is elliptical in shape. There are two parts (palpebral and orbital), with the paler palpebral part forming the eyelids.

Path: The orbital part is only attached to the medial walls of the orbital bones, and flows around the orbital rim to the zygomatic and maxillary bones.

Function: Closes the eyelids, as in winking, blinking and squinting. The orbicularis oculi is associated with a range of facial expressions and emotions, including laughter.

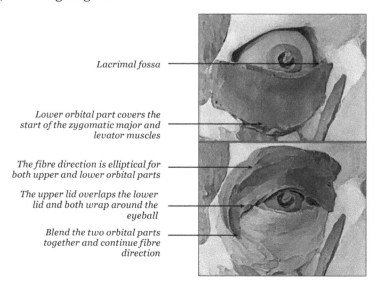

Lacrimal fossa

Lower orbital part covers the start of the zygomatic major and levator muscles

The fibre direction is elliptical for both upper and lower orbital parts

The upper lid overlaps the lower lid and both wrap around the eyeball

Blend the two orbital parts together and continue fibre direction

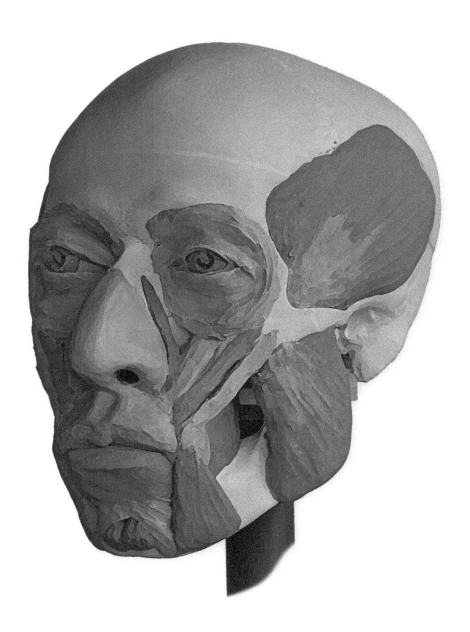

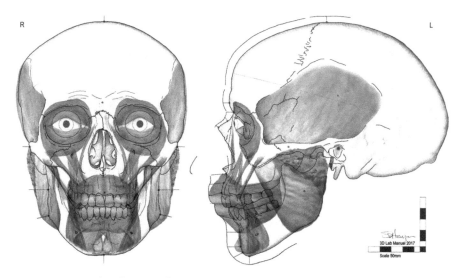

Parotid Gland

[G. para, near; otos, ear]

The largest of the salivary glands, the parotid may appear to be shaped like an inverted pyramid, but is highly variable in shape and size.

Path: The parotid can cover the zygomatic bone to the external auditory meatus (bony ear hole), part of the masseter muscle, and sometimes tapers down to the base of the jaw.

Function: A salivary gland with the duct opening inside the cheek, just opposite the second upper molar.

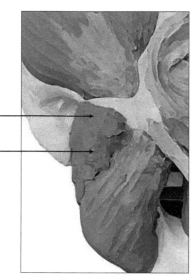

The superior part is in front of the ear hole and covers part of the zygomatic bone

The parotid is a globular mass highly variable in shape and size

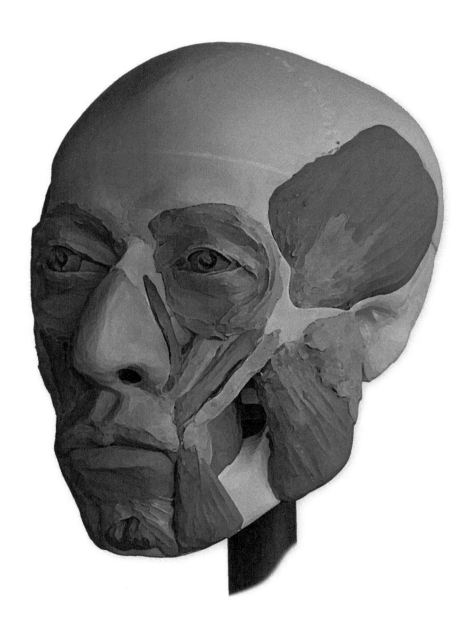

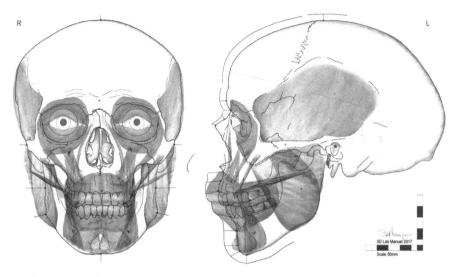

Risorius

[L. risus, laughter]

A very thin, delicate muscle. Although the word comes from the Latin for laughter, the risorius is often simply called the 'lip stretcher'.

Path: Arising in the fascia that covers the parotid gland, the risorius crosses the cheeks and inserts into the mouth at the modiolus (mouth hub).

Function: Pulls the lips laterally to widen the mouth, and can be associated with a sardonic facial expression.

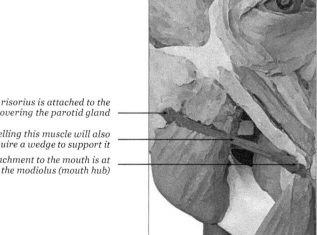

The risorius is attached to the sheath covering the parotid gland

Modelling this muscle will also require a wedge to support it

The attachment to the mouth is at the modiolus (mouth hub)

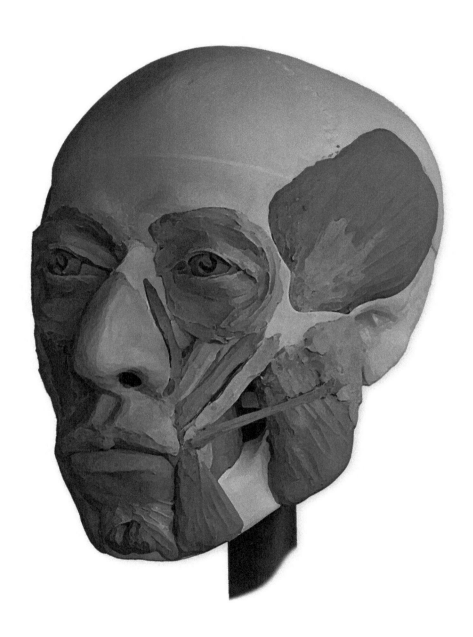

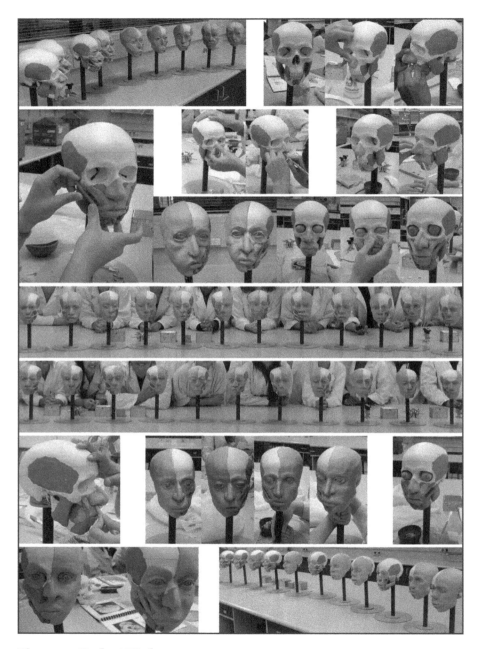

Figure 10. Student Work.
Between 2008-2013 I delivered a practicum for undergraduate forensic science students at Murdoch University in Western Australia. The students (three groups of about 24 students per group) worked in pairs and completed their work in five hours. These images are from May 2011, which was the first time A20 was the model for this undergraduate course. Photographs reproduced with kind permission of Professor Bob Mead.

PART B:
SURFACE APPEARANCE

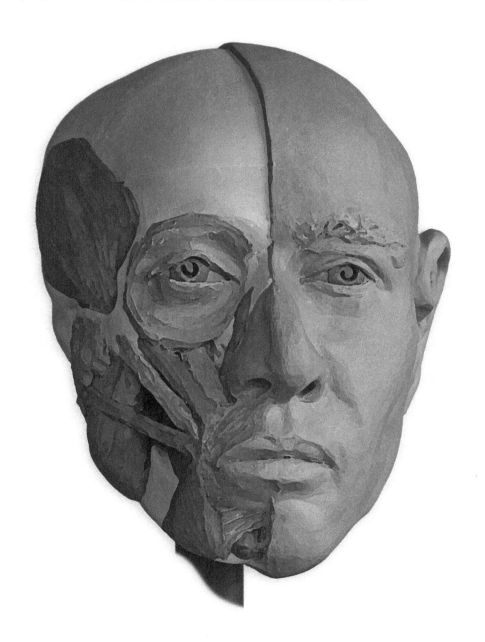

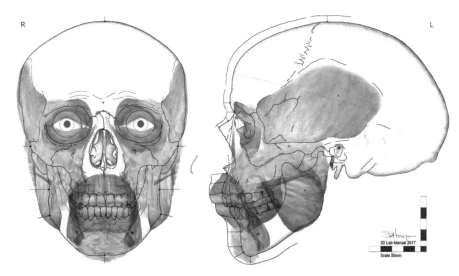

Facial Fat

Most of the fat in the face is located in the cheeks. The buccal fat pad is located between the buccinator and the masseter, with a temporal extension. Other main components of facial fat include orbital fat, the malar fat pad, the nasolabial fold, the temporal fat pad, jowl fat, and the fat of the chin region.

When modelling the face the fat is first blocked in to fill out the cheeks, then added to the nasolabial fold, 'cheek bones', upper eye and chin. These fatty areas mainly support the skin layer but do add some aspects of facial morphology referred to above.

References: Dumont et al. 2007, Rohrich and Pessa 2007.

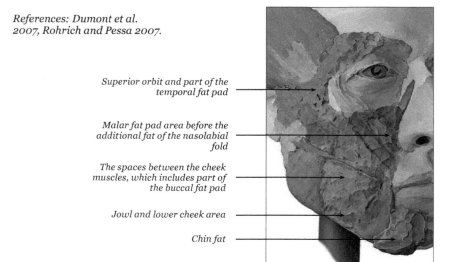

Superior orbit and part of the temporal fat pad

Malar fat pad area before the additional fat of the nasolabial fold

The spaces between the cheek muscles, which includes part of the buccal fat pad

Jowl and lower cheek area

Chin fat

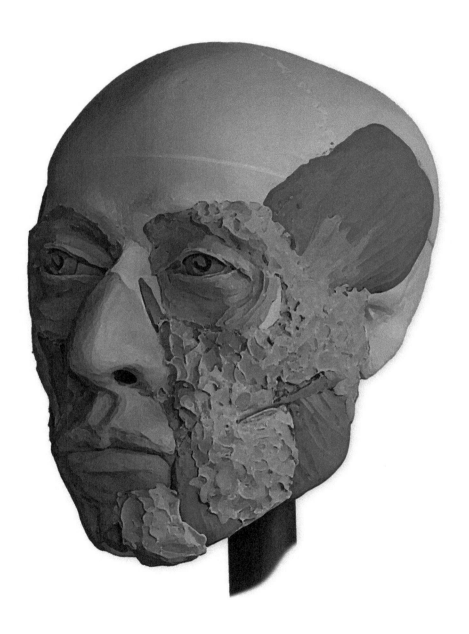

53

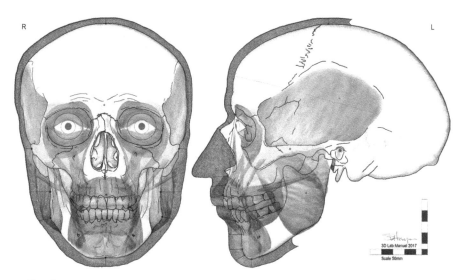

Skin

Modelling the skin layer involves rolling the clay out to a reasonably uniform depth, which is then placed over the anatomical model in sections. It may be easier starting with the nasolabial fold. Areas not covered by this skin layer include the nose, eyes and mouth, because these have already been modelled as surface features. Once the skin sections have covered half the face (or full face if desired), they can be joined and the overall surface smoothed.

References: Prag and Neave
1997, Taylor and Angel 1998

Start with a
triangular piece
that approximately
forms the
nasolabial fold

Continue adding
strips to cover the
face and then blend

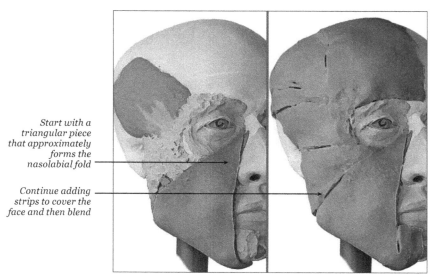

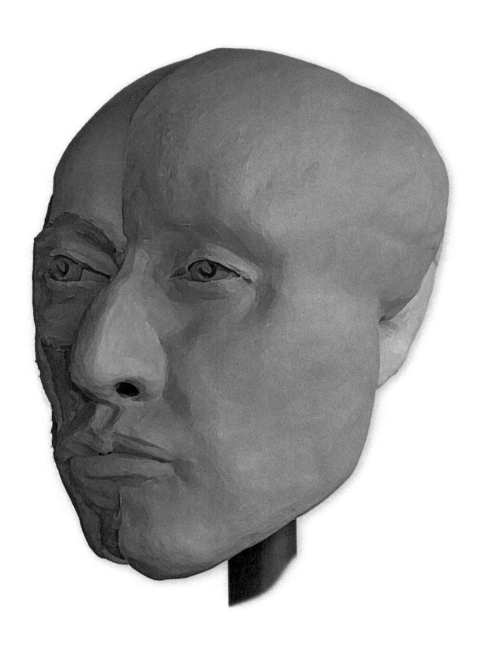

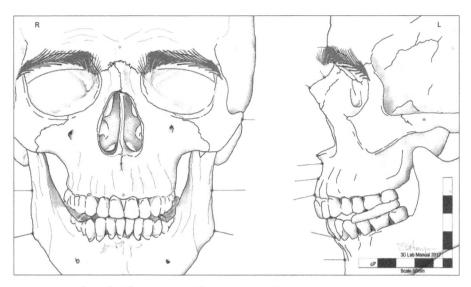

Eyefold and Eyebrow

The upper lid fold and the position of the eyebrow may be influenced by the shape of the superior orbital rim, and in some cases both may follow the general direction of the rim. The direction of eyebrow hairs is not uniform, and it has been suggested that they vary in both direction and density according to their position across the brow.

References: Fedosyutkin and Nainys 1993, Gerasimov 1955, Speed 1917.

The upper lid fold can be modelled using a strip of clay which is blended into the eye lid

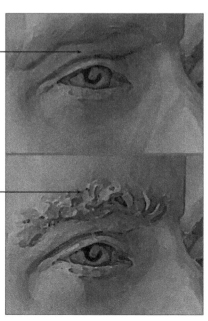

Rather than carving out the eyebrows, they can be suggested using small strips of clay

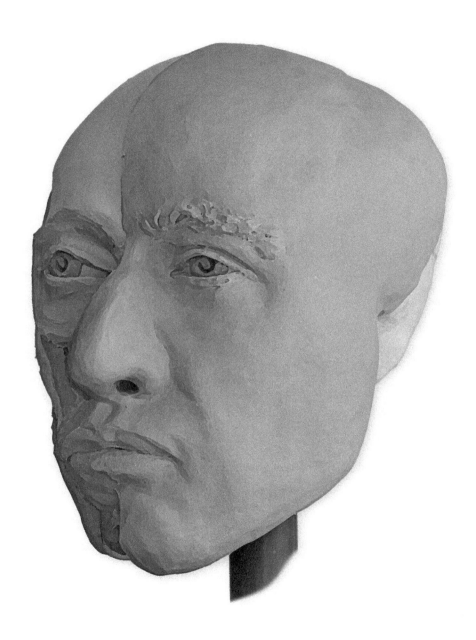

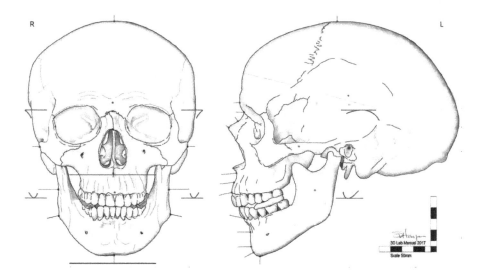

R   L

3D Lab Manual 2017
Scale 50mm

EARS

The height of the ear generally corresponds with the distance between the base of the nose and the bottom of the chin in young European adults (but not older adults, see Hayes *et al.* 2017), and the fleshy ear hole is located behind the external auditory meatus.

All of the *forensic facial reconstruction* recommendations for estimating ear size and angle are now known to be scientifically invalid, though the forensic artist Karen T. Taylor (2001) illustrates an excellent method for effectively sculpting an ear-like shape.

References: Guyomarc'h et al. 2012, Farkas and Munro 1987, Taylor 2001.

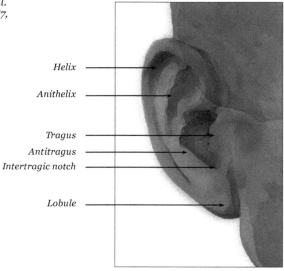

Helix

Anithelix

Tragus

Antitragus

Intertragic notch

Lobule

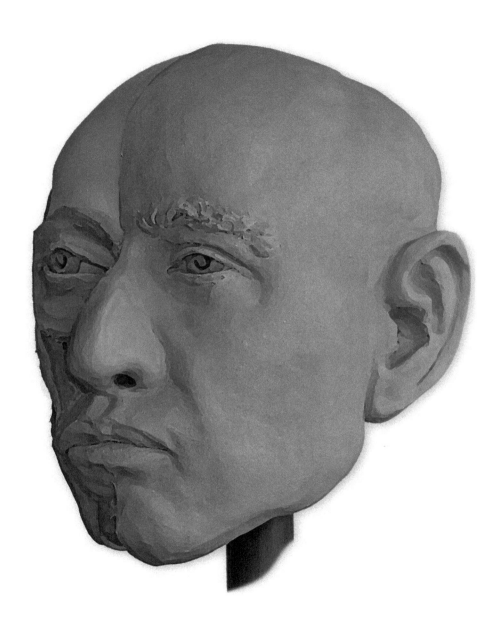

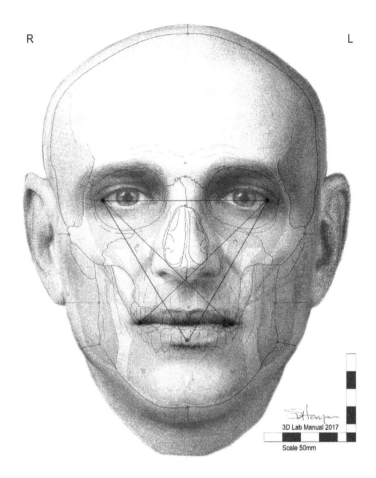

R   L

3D Lab Manual 2017
Scale 50mm

Facial Proportions

Robert George (1993, 2007) suggests that while most artistic canons do not apply to many human faces, both the 'Facial Triangle' and the 'Facial X' can be used as a general guide for cross-checking the main dimensions and locations of the facial features (eyes, nose, mouth) after a face has been estimated.

Facial Triangle: a roughly equilateral triangle is formed when three lines connect the outer corner of the eyes to each other, and each eye corner to the centre of the lower lip.

Facial X: two lines connecting each outer eye corner to the opposite mouth corner generally intersect at the base of the nasal septum.

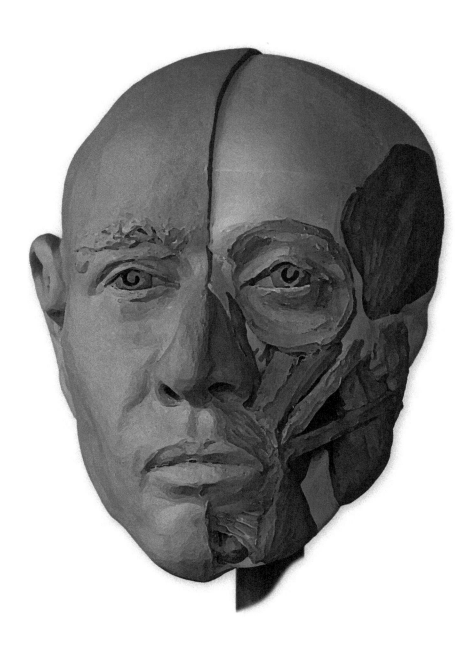

3D Lab Manual 2017

Scale 50mm

HAIR

For many years I resisted applying scalp hair to archaeological estimations because there are no known correlates between skull shape and hair colour, texture and style (e.g. Hayes *et al.* 2011). However, when shown a facial estimation with a hairless head, most people assume they are looking at a man — which was not particularly fair to the women I've worked with. My first inclusion of scalp hair was for the holotype (Liang Bua 1) of *Homo floresiensis* (Hayes *et al.* 2013). The late, great research archaeologist and colleague, Professor Mike Morwood, was the leader of the Indonesian-Australian excavation that discovered 'Hobbit' in 2003. Mike specifically asked that we don't do bald. After much thought I went for 'wet hair, off the face' to minimise the information, and have since applied modifications of this style to other facial estimations, including this revision of A20.

For students, applying a hairstyle allows for some relatively open creativity after a period of intensive and highly structured work (see examples on the next page). Scalp and facial hair (beards, moustaches) can also be helpful in covering up the occasional, and unintended, sculptural blemish.

Figure 11. Hair Work.
Participants from different 3D Labs showing variation in how head and facial hair can be sculpted.
Images reproduced with kind permission of the Museum Geologi Bandung, University of Wollongong, Balcatta Senior High School and the University of The Philippines (Archaeological Studies Program).

R   L

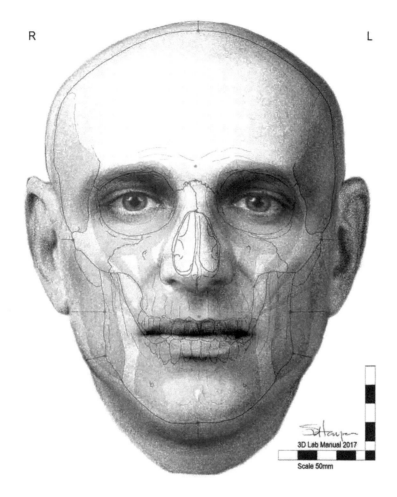

3D Lab Manual 2017

Scale 50mm

Figure 12. A20 Frontal Estimation.

REFERENCES

Anderson, K. J., M. Henneberg, and R. M. Norris. 2008. Anatomy of the nasal profile. **Journal of Anatomy** 213 (2):210-216.

Aulsebrook, W. A., P. J. Becker and M. Yagar 1996. Facial soft-tissue thicknesses in the adult male Zulu. **Forensic Science International** 79:83-102.

Cunha, E., E. Baccino, L. Martrille, F. Ramsthaler, J. Prieto, Y. Schuliar, N. Lynnerup and C. Cattaneo 2009. The problem of aging human remains and living individuals: A review. **Forensic Science International** 193(1): 1-13.

Duchenne de Boulogne, G.-B. 1990. **The Mechanism of Human Facial Expression**. Ed. & Trans. R. A. Cuthbertson. Cambridge, Cambridge University Press.

Dumont, T., E.. Simon, M. Stricker, J. L. Kahn and J. F. Chassagne 2007. Facial fat: Descriptive and functional anatomy, from a review of literature and dissections of 10 split-faces. **Annales de Chirurgie Plastique et Esthetique** 52(1)51-61.

Farkas, L. G. and I. R. Munro 1987. **Anthropometric Facial Proportions in Medicine**. Springfield, Charles C. Thomas.

Fedosyutkin, B. and J. Nainys 1993. The relationship of skull morphology to facial features. **Forensic Analysis of the Skull: Craniofacial Analysis, Reconstruction, and Identification**. Eds M. Y. Iscan and R. P. Helmer. New York, Wiley-Liss:119-213.

George, R. M. 2007. **Facial Geometry: Graphic Facial Analysis for Forensic Artists**. Springfield Illinois, Charles C. Thomas.

George, R. M. 1993. Anatomical and artistic guidelines for forensic facial reconstruction. **Forensic Analysis of the Skull: Craniofacial Analysis, Reconstruction, and Identification**. Eds M. Y. Iscan and R. P. Helmer. New York, Wiley-Liss:215-227.

Gerasimov, M. M. 1955. **The Reconstruction of the Face from the Basic Structure of the Skull**. Trans. W. Tshernezky 1975. Moscow, Nauka.

Guyomarc'h, P. and C. N. Stephan. 2012. The validity of ear prediction guidelines used in facial approximation. **Journal of Forensic Sciences** 57(6) 1427-1441.

Hayes, S, R. Shoocongdej, N. Pureepatpong, S. Sangvichien and C. Kanoknart. 2017. A Late Pleistocene woman from Tham Lod, Thailand: The influence of today on a face from the past. **Antiquity** 91(356):289-303.

Hayes, S. 2016. Faces in the museum: Revising the methods of facial reconstructions. **Museum Management and Curatorship** 31(3):218-245.

Hayes, S. 2014. Facial approximation of 'Angel': Case specific methodological review. **Forensic Science International** 237:e30-e41.

Hayes, S. 2012. **3D Facial Approximation: An Introductory Lab Manual** (AME1.0). Perth:UniPrint.

Hayes, S., H. Buckley, R. Bradley, N. Milne and J. Dennison. 2012. Approximating the face of 'Aunty': A question of likeness. **Journal of Archaeological Method and Theory** 19(2):1-16.

Hayes, S., T. Sutikna and M. Morwood 2013. Faces of *Homo floresiensis* (LB1). **Journal of Archaeological Science** 40 (12):4400-4410.

Hayes, S. 2011. **Introduction to Facial Approximation 2D Lab Manual** (AMV1.0). Perth:UniPrint.

Hayes, S., R. Taylor and A. Paterson 2005. Forensic facial approximation: An overview of current methods used at the Victorian Institute of Forensic Medicine/Victoria Police Criminal Identification Squad. **Journal of Forensic Odonto-Stomatology** 23(2):45-50.

Johnson, A., D. G. Wildgoose, and D. J. Wood 2002. The determination of freeway space using two different methods. **Journal of Oral Rehabilitation** 29(10):1010-1013.

Lisowski, F. P. and C. E. Oxnard 2007. **Anatomical Terms and their Derivation**. Singapore, World Scientific.

Mala, P. Z. 2013. Pronasale position: An appraisal of two recently proposed methods for predicting nasal projection in facial reconstruction. **Journal of Forensic Sciences** 58(4):957-963.

McMinn, R. M., R. T. Hutchings and B. M. Logan 1999. **Colour Atlas of Head and Neck Anatomy**, 2nd Ed. Edinburgh: Mosby-Wolfe.

Prag, J. and R. Neave 1993. **Making Faces: Using Forensic and Archaeological Evidence**. Texas: A & M University Press.

Rohrich, R. J. and J. E. Pessa 2007. The fat compartments of the face: Anatomy and clinical implications for cosmetic surgery. **Plastic and Reconstructive Surgery** 119(7):2219-2227.

Rynn, C., C. M. Wilkinson and H. Peters 2009. Prediction of nasal morphology from the skull. **Forensic Science, Medicine and Pathology** 61:20.

Song, W.-C., S.-H. Kim, D.-J. Paik, S.-H. Han, K.-S. Hu, H.-J. Kim and K.-S. Koh. 2007. Location of the infraorbital and mental foramen with reference to the soft-tissue landmarks. **Plastic and Reconstructive Surgery** 120 (5):1343-1347.

Speed, H. 1917. **The Practice and Science of Drawing**. 3rd Ed. New York, Dover.

Standring, S., Ed. 2008. **Gray's Anatomy: The Anatomical Basis of Clinical Practice**. 40th Ed. London, Elsevier.

Stephan, C. N. 2003. Facial approximation: An evaluation of mouth-width determination. **American Journal of Physical Anthropology** 121(1): 48-57.

Stephan, C. N. 2002. Facial approximation: Globe projection guideline falsified by exophthalmometry literature. **Journal of Forensic Sciences** 47(4):730-735.

Stephan, C. N., A. J. R. Huang and P. L. Davidson. 2009. Further evidence on the anatomical placement of the human eyeball for facial approximation and craniofacial superimposition. **Journal of Forensic Sciences** 54(2): 267-269.

Stephan, C. N. and E. K. Simpson 2008. Facial soft tissue depths in craniofacial identification (Part 1): An analytical review of the published adult data. **Journal of Forensic Sciences** 53(6):1257-1272.

Taylor, K. T. 2001. **Forensic Art and Illustration**. Boca Raton, CRC Press.

Taylor, R. G. and C. Angel 1998. Facial reconstruction and approximation. **Craniofacial Identification in Forensic Medicine**. Eds J. G. Clement and D. L. Ranson. London, Arnold:177-186.

Ullrich, H. and C. Stephan 2011. On Gerasimov's plastic facial reconstruction technique: New insights to facilitate repeatability. **Journal of Forensic Sciences** 56(2):470-474.

Warwick R. and P. Williams, Ed. 1973. **Gray's Anatomy: The Anatomical Basis of Clinical Practice**. 35th Ed. Edinburgh, Longman.

Whitnall, S. E. 1911. On a tubercle on the malar bone, and on the lateral attachments of the tarsal plates. **Journal of Anatomy and Physiology** 45 (Pt 4):426.

Wilkinson, C., M. Motwani and E. Chiang 2003. The relationship between the soft tissues and the skeletal detail of the mouth. **Journal of Forensic Sciences** 48(4):728-232.

Wolff, E. 1948. **The Anatomy of the Eye and Orbit**. 3rd Ed. London, H. K. Lewis.

ACKNOWLEDGEMENTS

Over a decade ago I worked with Ronn Taylor, the forensic sculptor for the Victorian Institute of Forensic Medicine, delivering 3D weekend workshops for the general public, hosted by the Victorian College of the Arts in Melbourne (for an overview of Ronn's work, see Hayes *et al.* 2005; Taylor and Angel, 1998). In 2006, an extended course was trialled working with Lance Byfield and his gifted students attending the Primary Extension and Challenge (PEAC) courses in the North Metropolitan Education Region of Perth, Western Australia. This used a very quirky replica skull, X104, and the input from Lance and his students (likewise quirky, but in a different way) was invaluable.

In 2011, X104 was retired from active clay duties, but is still the model for a 2D drawing course and Lab Manual (Hayes, 2011; also being revised and updated). The instructional methods have changed over the past decade, but the enjoyment and enthusiasm of the participants has remained the same. This section is to acknowledge the input of the living: the artists, anatomists, anthropologists, animators, archaeologists, biologists, dentists, geologists, museologists, massage therapists, police officers, forensic artists and scientists, primary, secondary and tertiary teachers and students, and members of the general public, who I got to know between 2006-2016. Many of these participants were instrumental in the development of the original 3D Lab Manual, and some have successfully used the Manual to deliver very popular art and forensic science courses of their own:

Australian Archaeological Association (2012); National Visual Arts Association (2012); Art Gallery of South Australia (2011); Art Gallery of Western Australia (1) (2010), National Portrait Gallery, Canberra1 (2011); Museum Geologi Bandung Indonesia (2) (2013); Sci-Tech Discovery Centre (3) (2012); Western Australian Museum (2007); The National Trust of Western Australia (2012); Edith Cowan University (2009-10, 2012); Murdoch University (2008-2012); Sheffield University (2016); University of The Philippines (4) (2014); University of Western Australia (2007-11); University of Wollongong (2012-2015); Kimberley Institute of Technology (3) (2012), Atwell Studio (2012); The Courthouse Gallery (3) (2012); Matans Studio (2010-11); Rockingham Regional Arts Group (2009); NSW Pottery Supplies (2013); Balcatta Senior High School Gifted & Talented Visual Art (5), with special thanks to Jamie Arkeveld (2011); North Metropolitan PEAC, with special thanks to Lance Byfield (2006-11).

1. *National Science Week, an Australian Government Initiative*
2. *Centre for Archaeological Science Small Grant, University of Wollongong Australia*
3. *Inspiring Australia, Public Science Communication for the Australian Department of Industry, Science and Research*
4. *Erasmus Mundi Visiting Fellow 2014, Archaeological Studies Program, University of The Philippines*
5. *AIR Grants Program project 2010-2011 assisted by the Federal Government through the Australia Council for the Arts and the Western Australian State Government through the Department of Culture and the Arts and Department of Education*